Waybuloo™

This annual belongs to

....

Age

....

Favourite Pipling

....

Waybuloo™
Annual 2012

EGMONT
We bring stories to life

First published in Great Britain 2011
by Egmont UK Limited,
239 Kensington High Street, London W8 6SA
Waybuloo ™ & © 2011
The Foundation TV Productions Limited/Decode/Blue Entertainment.
Licensed by Zodiak Rights.
With the support of the MEDIA Programme of the European Union
Written by Jenny Bak. Designed by Pritty Ramjee.

ISBN 978 1 4052 5706 0
1 3 5 7 9 10 8 6 4 2
Printed in Italy

Adult supervision is recommended when glue, paint, scissors and other sharp points are in use.

Contents

Hi Hi!

The Piplings are so happy to see you! This annual is packed with loads of Waybuloo puzzles, games and stories with your favourite Piplings. Come on, join the fun!

All answers can be found on page 68.

A friendly frog is leaping through the pages of this book. Colour in one lily pad each time you spot him.

Lau Lau

Lau Lau loves to paint pictures. Help her make some new paint by colouring in the splashes below with new colours.

 +  =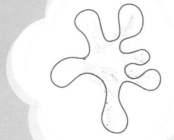

blue + yellow = green

 + =

red + blue = purple

 + =

yellow + red = orange

Yojojo

Yojojo likes to make music for his friends.
Can you find his musical instruments?
Tick the boxes as you find each one.

"play music with Yojojo!"

trumpet

whistle

drum

9

De Li

De Li grows beautiful flowers in her garden. Count how many narabugs and flowers you can see below, then colour them in.

"De Li love pretty flowers!"

10

Nok Tok

Nok Tok likes to make things for his friends.
Can you colour in only the tools that
belong in his toolbox?

"Nok Tok can mend anything!"

Come Play, Narabug!

Yojojo is whistling to call his narabug
to come play. Which winding path
should it take to get to him?

Picture Play

Lau Lau is painting a picture of a flower. Draw some more flowers, then colour in the picture.

Jumpy Seeds

"**Hi hi! De Li count jumpy seeds today.**"
De Li picks up the wiggly, jiggly seeds and puts them in her bowl.
"**One, two, three ...**" she counts slowly.

"**Hi hi!**"
Nok Tok comes to help plant the seeds in pots. He pokes holes in the soil.
"**One, two, three,**" he says. Uh-oh ... De Li loses count of her jumpy seeds!

De Li tries to count again. But soon Yojojo comes along. **"Watch Yojojo!"** he shouts as he bounces around. Oops ... De Li has lost count of the jumpy seeds again!

De Li goes to a quiet place to try again. **"Present for De Li!"** says Lau Lau. She holds up a pretty picture she has made. Uh-oh ... De Li has lost count again!

De Li is sad that she can't count the jumpy seeds. Then, the cheebies come to Nara! They help De Li count her seeds.

1 2 3 4 5
6 7 8 9 10

There are 10 jumpy seeds!

Next, the Piplings and cheebies plant the jumpy seeds. They put a seed in each pot, then cover it with soil.

The pots wiggle, jiggle and jump in the air ... so the cheebies wiggle, jiggle and jump up, too!

Suddenly, beautiful flowers grow out of the pots. When the flowers bloom, lots of jumpy seeds pop into the air!

"1, 2, 3 ... too many jumpy seeds to count!" De Li laughs. The Piplings are so happy that they float up into the air. **Waybuloo!**

Strawberry Search

De Li wants to pick some sweet strawberries to share with her Pipling friends. Can you show her the way to the strawberry bush?

start ⇨

⇨ finish

Pip Speak

Draw lines to match the Piplings to the things they say.

b.
Love to paint pictures with cheebies!

a.
Music makes Piplings happy!

c.
Pretty flowers growing in garden!

d.
Pipling tools can mend anything!

Time for Yogo!

Nok Tok and De Li are doing yogo.
You try!

Bridge

Lie on your back. Keep your hands and feet on the floor. Lift up your body so it looks like a bridge.

Snail

Kneel on the floor with your knees apart, then reach backwards and grab your feet.

21

Make a Bird Feeder

This birdfeeder will give the birds a tasty treat!
Ask an adult to help you with each step.

You will need:
Empty milk carton
Masking tape
Paint
Paintbrush
Safety scissors
Unsharpened pencil
Birdseed
String

1

Tape the top shut on
the milk carton. Paint
it your favourite colour
and let it dry.

2

Cut a hole on one side,
big enough for a bird.

3 Ask an adult to poke a pencil through the carton, about 2cm below the hole.

4 Decorate the carton however you'd like. Use bright colours that birds can spot!

5 Put some birdseed in the hole.

6 Poke a hole through the carton top to tie on some string. Then ask an adult to hang your birdfeeder from a tree branch, out of reach of children and cats. The birds will love their yummy snack!

23

The Tallest Pipling

"Hi hi, Nok Tok!"
"Hi hi, De Li!"
Nok Tok shows De Li
his new measuring
stick. **"Measure
De Li?"** he asks.

De Li stands
still while Nok Tok paints
a pink line on the stick to
show how tall she is. Just
then, they hear a tinkling
sound. **"Time for yogo!"**
says Nok Tok.

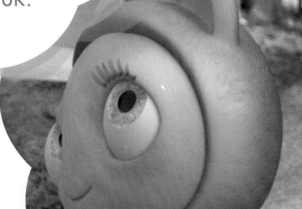

After yogo, Lau Lau finds the stick. **"Perfect to stir paint!"** she smiles. She breaks off a piece and hops away to her art studio.

Yojojo sees the stick next. **"Stick make good whistle!"** he laughs. He breaks off a piece and blows in it to make a sound. **Toot toot!** he plays as he runs off.

Nok Tok comes back and measures himself with the stick. De Li's pink line is much lower. **"Nok Tok much taller than De Li,"** he says. **"Nok Tok grow very fast!"**

Nok Tok wants to share the happy news with his Pipling friends. He brings them together and tells them, **"Nok Tok tallest Pipling in Nara!"**

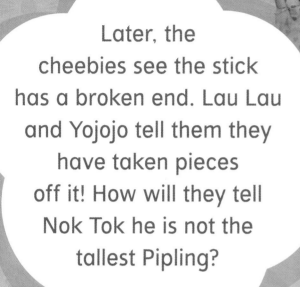

Later, the cheebies see the stick has a broken end. Lau Lau and Yojojo tell them they have taken pieces off it! How will they tell Nok Tok he is not the tallest Pipling?

At the same time, Nok Tok realises that if he grows too tall, he will not be able to share huggles with the Piplings anymore. **"No huggles make Nok Tok sad,"** he says.

The cheebies tell Nok Tok he is not the tallest Pipling in Nara. Everyone lines up, from tallest to shortest, so Nok Tok can see he is not too tall!

"**Nok Tok can huggle with Piplings!**" laughs Nok Tok. So the Piplings gather together and share a great big huggle. **Waybuloo!**

28

Tool Trick

Nok Tok needs a special tool to cut some wood.
Starting at number 1, join the dots to see what
tool he needs, then colour in the picture.

Caterpillar Quiz

Find two caterpillars that are
exactly the same.

Time for Yogo!

Lau Lau and Yojojo are doing yogo.
You try!

Boat

Sit on the floor with your legs straight out. Grab your feet and lift them up from the floor so you are balancing on your bottom, like a boat rocking on waves!

Big Roary Thing

Lean forward and make a roar like a big animal!

Yojojo's Jumpybug

You can help read this story. Listen to the words and when you come to a picture, say the name.

Lau Lau

Nok Tok

De Li

Yojojo

pipes

jumpybug

bush

One day,  is playing his  when

a  jumps from a nearby  .

"**Whoa!**" says  . He is so surprised that

he drops his  . **Jump!** goes the  .

Bounce! goes  after it. Soon, the other

Piplings come to play. **Jump!** goes the .

Bounce! goes  . **Hop!** goes  .

Leap! goes  . **Skip!** goes  .

Then, the  jumps away and the Piplings

can't find it!  asks, **"How**  **find**

 **before?"**  says, **"Thinkapow!**

Play song on  **!"**  looks for

his  , but they have gone missing, too.

He is very sad to lose both the and

his  !

Suddenly, the  comes back! It jumps this

way and that way, waiting for the Piplings to follow.

Jump! goes the . **Bounce!** goes .

Hop! goes . **Leap!** goes .

Skip! goes . The  leads the

Piplings to a  and jumps underneath.

 looks under the .

35

The  is sitting on the  ! "Thank

you,  !" says  . He is so happy

to find his  that he floats up into the air.

The other Piplings float up, too.

"Waybuloo!"

Colour Code

Colour in this picture of Nok Tok, using the colour code to help you.

Spot the Shapes

Circles, triangles and squares are kinds of shapes.
Draw lines to match the tambourine, neepnip and
easel to the shapes they look like.

tambourine

square

neepnip

circle

easel

triangle

Making Music

Yojojo loves to make music for his friends.
Colour in this picture of Yojojo
playing his banjojo.

Beautiful Nara

The Piplings live in a beautiful place called Nara.
These pictures of Nara look the same but 5 things
are different in picture 2. Can you spot them all?

Dancing Feet

"**Lau Lau love dancing!**" laughs Lau Lau as she jumps and spins in the air. "**Lau Lau want to paint dancing. But easel is broken.**"

The Piplings come to help. "**Nok Tok get hammer to mend easel,**" he says. This makes Lau Lau very happy! "**Thank you, Nok Tok!**"

Whilst they wait for Nok Tok, De Li has an idea. **"Lau Lau draw De Li and Yojojo dancing!"** So Lau Lau draws a picture of them dancing together.

Nok Tok brings back a special gift for Lau Lau – a music box! It has a tiny doll that spins round and round. Lau Lau quickly draws the dancing doll.

43

But when Lau Lau looks at her two drawings, she says, **"Pictures don't look like dancing. Wish cheebies here to help!"**

Just then, the cheebies come! "We'll help you, Lau Lau," they say. "You can draw us dancing!" So Nok Tok bangs his hammer and Yojojo plays his pipes to make happy dancing music!

Uh-oh! One of the cheebies knocks over a paint pot. Red paint spills on Lau Lau's paper. "I'm sorry, Lau Lau," says the cheebie.

Thinkapow! A clever cheebie has an idea. She takes off her shoes and steps in the spilled paint. Then she dances all over the paper. The other cheebies join in!

The cheebies spill green and yellow paint, then dance some more. "Lau Lau, look at our picture," say the cheebies when they are finished.

"**Painting look just like dancing!**" smiles Lau Lau. "**Best picture ever!**" All the Piplings are so happy they float up into the air. **Waybuloo!**

Time for Yogo!

Nok Tok and De Li are doing yogo.
You try!

Owl

Kneel on the ground and sit back on your feet. Slowly rise up on your knees and lift your arms above your head, then sit back down down your feet and lower your arms, like an owl flapping its wings.

Cat

Kneel down with your hands on the floor. Slowly lift your head and arch your back like a cat stretching.

Funny Faces

Draw funny faces on these Piplings! Can you draw a smiling Pipling and a frowning Pipling?

What's Wrong?

There are three mistakes in this picture.
Point to them as you find them.

Make a Maraca

Make some music with this simple maraca!
Ask an adult to help you with each step.

You will need:
Water bottle
Masking tape
Paint
Paintbrush
Marker pens
Paper for funnel
Rice

Wrap an empty, travel-size water bottle with masking tape, leaving the cap free.

Decorate the covered bottle using paint or markers, and let dry.

3

Put two handfuls of uncooked rice into the bottle. A paper funnel makes it easier.

4

Replace the cap tightly, then shake, shake, shake to make some noise, just like Yojojo!

Garden Game

De Li is working in her lovely garden. Tick only the things that she needs to make her garden grow!

watering can

trowel

whistle

paint pot

52

Back to Front

The Piplings have turned around so you can't see their faces! Draw lines to match their pictures to their names.

a

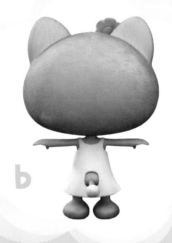

b

c

d

De Li

Lau Lau

Nok Tok

Yojojo

Whizzcrackers

In Nara, colourful whizzcrackers suddenly fly across the sky! **Swish! Swoosh!**

Yojojo hears the sound and runs outside, but the whizzcrackers have gone. He lays on a big rock to wait for them to come back.

Just then, Nok Tok comes with three singballs. Yojojo juggles them to make music! One of them rolls away, and he runs off to find it.

"Look, whizzy whizzcrackers!" cries Lau Lau, pointing to the sky. She and Nok Tok watch the pretty lights. Yojojo rushes back, but he's too late to see them!

Yojojo lays on the rock again, but soon his narabug comes to play. Yojojo dances with his narabug, then follows it behind a tree.

"Whizzcrackers there!" De Li shouts to Nok Tok and Lau Lau. They look for Yojojo, but he's not there. He has missed the whizzcrackers again!

The cheebies come and wait with Yojojo. They look up into the sky, but there are no whizzcrackers. Thinkapow! Nok Tok has an idea!

"**Find bongleberries to put in Anything Machine**," Nok Tok tells his friends. "**Anything Machine will throw them in the air, like whizzcrackers!**"

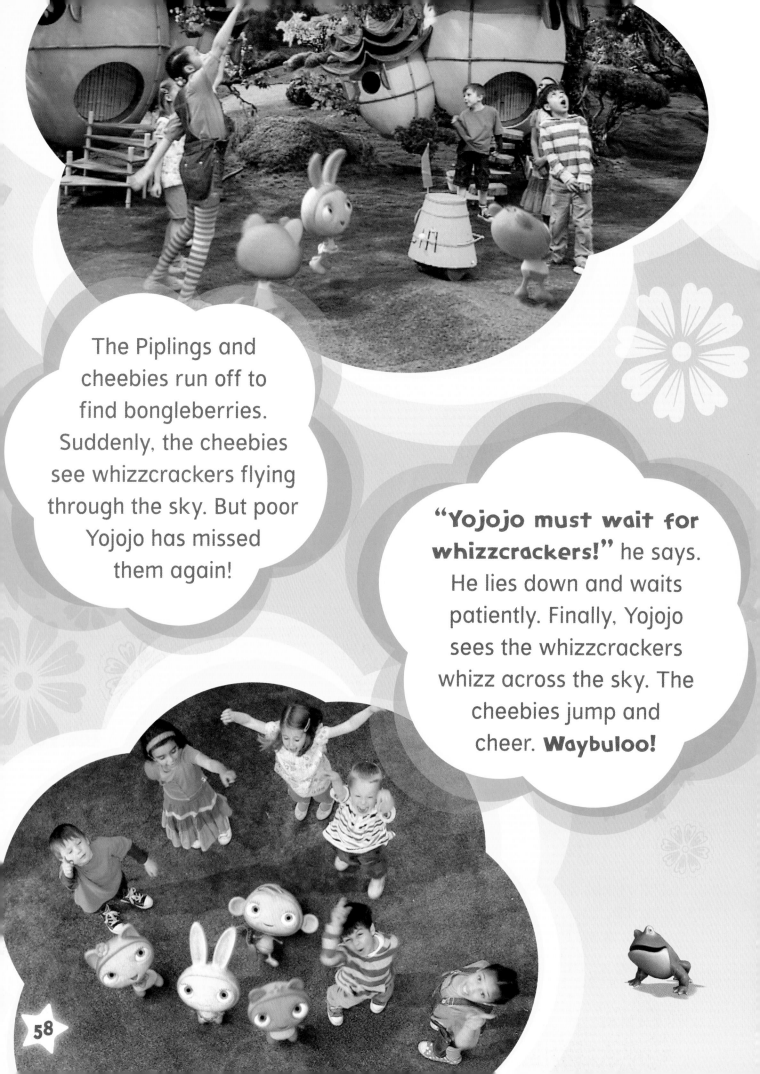

The Piplings and cheebies run off to find bongleberries. Suddenly, the cheebies see whizzcrackers flying through the sky. But poor Yojojo has missed them again!

"Yojojo must wait for whizzcrackers!" he says. He lies down and waits patiently. Finally, Yojojo sees the whizzcrackers whizz across the sky. The cheebies jump and cheer. **Waybuloo!**

Counting Crackers

Yojojo is watching the whizzcrackers fly
through the sky. Count the whizzcrackers,
then colour in the picture.

Eye Spy

All of the things in the small pictures can be found in the big picture. Tick the boxes as you find each one.

stork

paint pot

bananas

Time for Yogo!

Lau Lau and Yojojo are doing yogo.
You try!

Big Bird

While standing, lift your foot and hold it with your hand. Hold your other hand up and try to balance like a big bird!

Mouse

Kneel on the floor and sit back on your heels. Using your hands to help you, slowly lean forward until your head is on the ground, as low as a little mouse!

Waybuloo!

Which Pipling will win the buloo contest?

You will need:

A dice and counters for two to four players.

How to play:

Choose a Pipling and place your counters on the **start** spaces.

Take it in turns to roll the dice. The Pipling with the highest number can move their counter up one cloud. If two or more Piplings get the same number, roll again.

If you land on a space with a narabug, roll the dice again. The first player to float up to the top is the buloo winner!

start

start

start

start

Puzzle Break

Yojojo is collecting mangos to share with the cheebies. Point to the biggest mango, then point to the smallest.

The jumpybugs are having a hopping contest. Point to the one that's hopping the highest, then point to the one that's hopping the lowest.

Favourite Friend

Which Pipling is your favourite? Draw a picture of yourself and your Pipling friend here!

Let's Play Peeka!

De Li, Yojojo, Nok Tok and Lau Lau are playing peeka
with you! Draw a tick as you find each Pipling.

See You Soon!

The Piplings had a wonderful time playing with you!
Colour them in, then say goodbye!

Answers

P7: Find the Frogs
There are six frogs on pages 9, 14, 25, 28, 42, 58.

P9: Yojojo

P10: De Li
There are two narabugs and six flowers.

P11: Nok Tok
The spanner and saw belong in the toolbox.

P12: Come Play, Narabug!
Yojojo should take path **c**.

P19: Strawberry Search

P21: Pip Speak
a - Yojojo, **b** - Lau Lau,
c - De Li, **d** - Nok Tok.

P30: Caterpillar Quiz
Pictures **a** and **c** are exactly the same.

P38: Spot the Shapes
tambourine - circle, neepnip - triangle, easel - square.

P40-41: Beautiful Nara

P49: What's Wrong?
Narabug has square wings, Nok Tok is green and Yojojo has long ears.

P52: Garden Game
De Li needs a trowel and a watering can.

P53: Back to Front
a - Yojojo, **b** - De Li,
c - Lau Lau, **d** - Nok Tok.

P59: Cracker Count
There are six whizzcrackers.

P60: Eye Spy

P66: Let's Play Peeka!